Here We Go Round the Mulberry Bush

and Other Nursery Rhyme Games

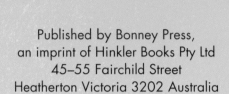

Published by Bonney Press,
an imprint of Hinkler Books Pty Ltd
45–55 Fairchild Street
Heatherton Victoria 3202 Australia
www.hinkler.com.au

**BONNEY
PRESS**

© Hinkler Books Pty Ltd 2015

Illustrators: Steph Baxter, Sarah Coleman, Sarah Dennis, Lauren Hom, Lalalimola, Mick Marston, Jess Matthews, Chris Robertson, Marie Simpson, Alice Stevenson, Yulia Vysotskaya.

ISBN: 978 1 7436 3813 2

Printed and bound in China

Contents

Here we go round the mulberry bush,
The mulberry bush, the mulberry bush.
Here we go round the mulberry bush,
On a cold and frosty morning.

This is the way we wash our clothes,
Wash our clothes, wash our clothes.
This is the way we wash our clothes,
On a cold and frosty morning.

London Bridge is falling down,
Falling down, falling down.
London Bridge is falling down,
My fair lady.

Build it up with sticks and stones,
Sticks and stones, sticks and stones...

Sticks and stones will wear away,
Wear away, wear away...

Build it up with iron and steel,
Iron and steel, iron and steel...

Iron and steel will bend and bow,
Bend and bow, bend and bow...

Build it up with bricks and clay,
Bricks and clay, bricks and clay...

Bricks and clay will wash away,
Wash away, wash away...

Build it up with silver and gold,
Silver and gold, silver and gold...

Silver and gold will be stole away,
Stole away, stole away...

London Bridge is falling down,
Falling down, falling down...

A-TISKET, A-TASKET, A green and yellow BASKET. I WROTE a LETTER to MY love, AND ON THE WAY, I DROPPED IT.

I DROPPED IT, I DROPPED it, AND ON THE way, I DROPPED IT. A little BOY PICKED it UP, AND PUT it in HIS POCKET.

Half a pound of tuppenny rice,
Half a pound of treacle.
That's the way the money goes,
Pop goes the weasel!

Every night when I get home
The monkey's on the table.
Take a stick and knock it off,
Pop goes the weasel!

Up and down the City Road
In and out the Eagle.
That's the way the money goes,
Pop goes the weasel!

All around the mulberry bush
The monkey chased the weasel.
The monkey stopped to pull up his sock,
Pop goes the weasel!

The farmer in the dell,
The farmer in the dell,
Hey-ho, the derry-o,
The farmer in the dell.

The farmer takes a wife...

The wife takes the child...

The child takes the nurse...

The nurse takes the cow...

The cow takes the dog...

The dog takes the cat...

The cat takes the mouse...

The mouse takes the cheese...

The cheese stands alone...

PEASE PORRIDGE HOT,
PEASE PORRIDGE COLD,
PEASE PORRIDGE IN THE POT,
NINE DAYS OLD;
SOME LIKE IT HOT, SOME LIKE IT COLD,
SOME LIKE IT IN THE POT,
NINE DAYS OLD.

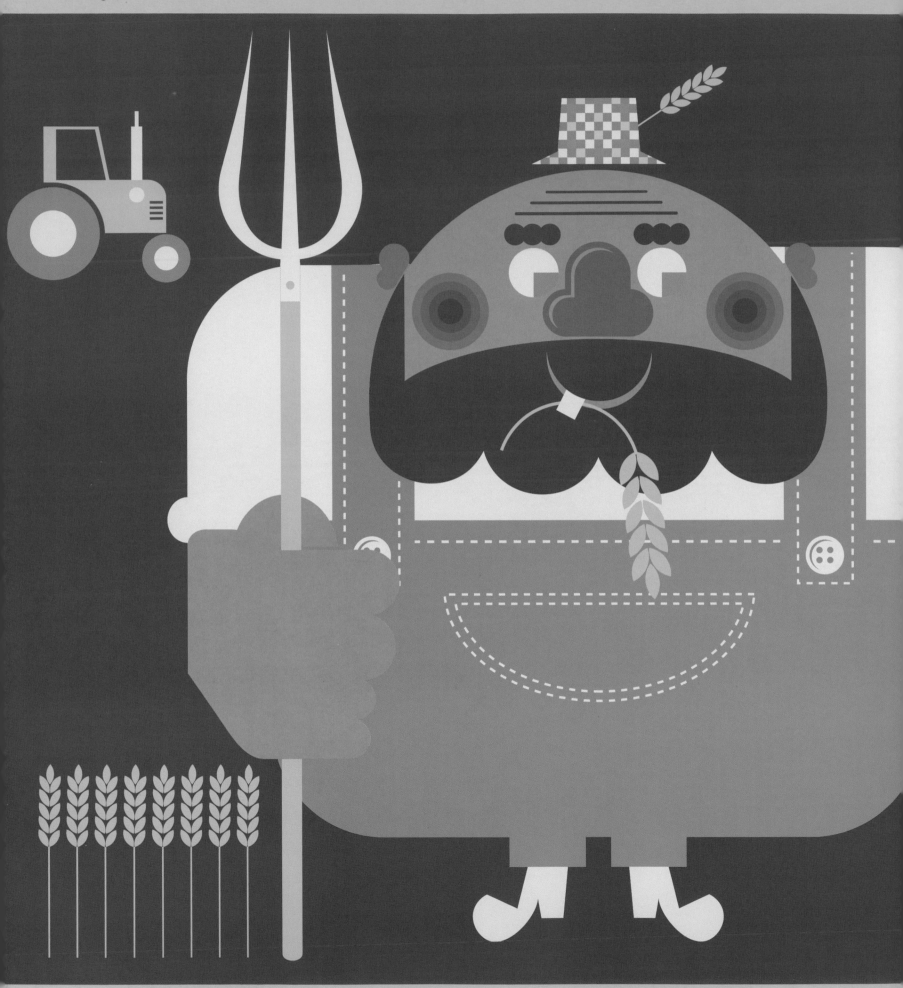

There was a farmer had a dog,
And Bingo was his name-o.
B-I-N-G-O!
B-I-N-G-O!
B-I-N-G-O!
And Bingo was his name-o!

There was a farmer had a dog...
(clap)-I-N-G-O! (x 3)
And Bingo was his name-o!

There was a farmer had a dog...
(clap)-(clap)-N-G-O! (x 3)
And Bingo was his name-o!

There was a farmer had a dog...
(clap)-(clap)-(clap)-G-O! (x 3)
And Bingo was his name-o!

There was a farmer had a dog...
(clap)-(clap)-(clap)-(clap)-O! (x 3)
And Bingo was his name-o!

There was a farmer had a dog...
(clap)-(clap)-(clap)-(clap)-(clap)! (x 3)
And Bingo was his name-o!

A sailor went to sea, sea, sea,
To see what he could see, see, see;
But all that he could see, see, see,
Was the bottom of the deep blue sea, sea, sea!

A sailor went to chop, chop, chop,
To see what he could chop, chop, chop;
But all that he could chop, chop, chop,
Was the bottom of the deep blue chop, chop, chop!

A sailor went to knee, knee, knee,
To see what he could knee, knee, knee;
But all that he could knee, knee, knee,
Was the bottom of the deep blue knee, knee, knee!

A sailor went to sea, chop, knee,
To see what he could see, chop, knee;
But all that he could see, chop, knee,
Was the bottom of the deep blue sea, chop, knee!

CHORUS:
HERE WE GO LOOBY LOO,
HERE WE GO LOOBY LIGHT;
HERE we go looby loo,
ALL ON A SATURDAY NIGHT.

YOU PUT YOUR RIGHT ARM IN,
YOU PUT YOUR RIGHT ARM OUT;
YOU SHAKE IT A LITTLE, A LITTLE,
And turn yourself about.
CHORUS

YOU PUT YOUR LEFT ARM IN...

CHORUS

YOU PUT YOUR RIGHT LEG IN...

Chorus

YOU PUT YOUR LEFT LEG IN...

Chorus

YOU PUT YOUR WHOLE SELF IN...

CHORUS

Chorus:
Lou, Lou, skip to my Lou,
Lou, Lou, skip to my Lou,
Lou, Lou, skip to my Lou,
Skip to my Lou, my darling.

Fly's in the buttermilk, shoo fly shoo,
Fly's in the buttermilk, shoo fly shoo,
Fly's in the buttermilk, shoo fly shoo,
Skip to my Lou, my darling.
Chorus

Little red wagon, painted blue, (x 3)
Skip to my Lou, my darling.
Chorus

Lost my partner, what'll I do? (x3)
Skip to my Lou, my darling.
Chorus

I'll find another one, prettier than you, (x 3)
Skip to my Lou, my darling.
Chorus

Can't get a red bird, jay bird'll do, (x 3)
Skip to my Lou, my darling.
Chorus

Cat's in the cream jar, how they chew, (x 3)
Skip to my Lou, my darling.
Chorus

Pig's in the parlour, what'll I do? (x 3)
Skip to my Lou, my darling.
Chorus

Off to Texas, two by two, (x 3)
Skip to my Lou, my darling.
Chorus

'ORANGES and LEMONS',
SAY THE BELLS OF St. Clements.

'YOU OWE ME FIVE FARTHINGS',
SAY THE BELLS OF St. Martins.

'WHEN will YOU pay ME?'
SAY THE BELLS OF Old Bailey.

'WHEN I grow RICH',
SAY THE BELLS OF Shoreditch.

'WHEN *will* THAT *be*?'
SAY THE BELLS OF *Stepney*.

'I *do* NOT KNOW,'
SAYS THE GREAT BELL OF *Bow*.

HERE COMES *a* CANDLE *to* LIGHT YOU TO BED,
AND HERE COMES *a* CHOPPER *to* CHOP OFF *your* HEAD!

CHOP *CHOP* CHOP *CHOP*

THE LAST MAN'S DEAD!

Here We Go Round the Mulberry Bush (page 4)

Children dance in a circle for first verse. They act out washing clothes during second verse, then repeat first verse and circle dance. Sometime they will take it in turns to make up extra verses and act out the actions for each new verse.

London Bridge (page 6)

Two children make an arch with their arms. The others pass through the arch in single file, circling around to keep passing underneath. The 'arch' is then lowered at the end of each verse or at the song's end to 'catch' a player. The last player left is the winner.

A-Tisket, A-Tasket (page 8)

Children dance in a circle. One child runs around the outside of the circle and drops a 'letter' on the first 'I dropped it'. Whoever it is dropped next to then picks it up and chases the child who dropped it. The child who gets to the empty place first sits down and the other child then runs around the outside of the circle when the rhyme is sung the next time.

Pop Goes the Weasel (page 10)

Children form several circles and dance singing the verse, holding hands. Meanwhile, single players called 'weasels' stand in the middle of each ring, with one extra player roaming around the circles (so there is one more weasel than rings). When the children sing 'pop goes the weasel', they release their hands and the weasels run to stand inside a new circle. The weasel that doesn't make it into a circle is out, and the remaining players form one fewer ring and repeat, until there is only one weasel left as the winner.

The Farmer in the Dell (page 14)

The players form a circle holding hands around one who is designated as the farmer, singing the first verse while moving around. When the verse is over they stop and the farmer makes his choice of a wife (sometimes without looking). The wife joins him in the centre for her verse and so through the verses until either the cheese or dog is selected or only one person is left to become the last character. They usually become the farmer for the next round.

Ring-a-ring o' Roses (page 18)

Children hold hands and walk in a circle for the first three lines of the song. They all fall to the floor on 'We all fall down.'

Pease Porridge Hot (page 19)

Pease	(clap both hands to thighs)
porridge	(clap own hands together)
hot	(clap partner's hands)
Pease	(clap both hands to thighs)
porridge	(clap own hands together)
cold	(clap partner's hands)
Pease	(clap thighs)
porridge	(clap own hands)
in the	(clap right hands only)
pot	(clap own hands)
Nine	(clap left hands only)
days	(clap own hands)
old	(clap partner's hands)

Bingo (page 20)

Each verse the word B-I-N-G-O is spelled out, one letter is replaced with a clap, until all letters of the word are clapped.

A Sailor Went to Sea, Sea, Sea (page 22)

(shield your eyes one hand on each mention of the word 'sea/see')	A sailor went to sea, sea, sea...
(make a chopping motion on your arm on each mention of the word 'chop')	A sailor went to chop, chop, chop...
(tap your knee on each mention of the word 'knee')	A sailor went to knee, knee, knee...
(make each of the appropriate motions above on each mention of the words 'sea/see, chop, knee')	A sailor went to sea, chop, knee...

Here We Go Looby Loo (page 24)

Children dance in a circle for the 'looby loo' chorus. They stop for each verse and act out the instructions: putting the right arm in and out of the circle and shaking it, then turning around before singing the chorus and dancing in a circle again. This is repeated with the left arm, each leg, and finally their whole self, as they jump in and out of the circle.

Skip to My Lou (page 26)

Couples skip in a circle, hand in hand, with a single person in the middle of the circle. The single player sings the 'Lost my partner, what'll I do?' verse. Then the other players reply 'I'll find another one, prettier than you' and the single person grabs a partner from the closest couple. The new single person takes their place in the middle and the song repeats.

Oranges and Lemons (page 30)

Two children make an arch with their arms. The others form pairs and pass through the arch two by two, circling around to keep passing underneath. The arch is then lowered at the end of the song on 'dead!' to 'catch' a pair. The caught pair stands next the last pair and makes an arch. As the rhyme continues, each caught pair joins the arch, so it becomes longer and longer. The final pair is the winner.